# Welcome Aboa

Scholastic's **THE MAGIC SCHOOL BUS** is the new, animated science adventure series based on Scholastic's award-winning book series by Joanna Cole and Bruce Degen. Airing on **PBS**, the action-packed half-hour episodes are geared to six- to nine-year-olds, with educational and entertainment appeal for those younger and older.

Ride with Ms. Frizzle, teacher extraordinaire, and her enthusiastic, inquisitive students as their Magic School Bus takes them on cliff-hanging field trips into the human body, inside an ant colony, and far out into space. In thirteen episodes each season, **THE MAGIC SCHOOL BUS** transforms the world into a fresh and funny science laboratory—each time with a new destination.

Each show focuses on a single science idea captured in a dramatic adventure format. Driven by Ms. Frizzle and her multicultural class, the series shows all children, especially girls and minorities, that science is for everyone. As The Friz guides her class through each adventure, she encourages students to arrive at their own conclusions through experimentation and discovery, and helps them explore different ways to accomplish their goals.

This guide will help you build on the appeal of the series in support of your own science goals.

More than a television series, **THE MAGIC SCHOOL BUS** education effort encompasses a broad partnership of museums, youth-serving organizations, libraries, and schools. To find out about other ways you can get involved in **THE MAGIC SCHOOL BUS**, contact Jenny Lam, Director of Promotions and Outreach, at (212) 780-9831.

And be sure to look for the newest title in the book series, *THE MAGIC SCHOOL BUS in the Time of the Dinosaurs.*

## TIPS FOR VIEWING

- Plan ahead! See how many episodes fit your science program.
- Preview the episode before showing it to the children.
- Prepare children by asking them questions prior to viewing.
- Let students watch each episode all the way through.
- View more than once—and discuss the episode with children. Help them see how Ms. Frizzle gets her students to answer their own questions.

## GOALS:
- to motivate children's interest in science
- to inspire positive attitudes toward science and education
- to introduce science concepts and ideas

## SEE ALL THIRTEEN EPISODES
- Check your local TV listings to find out the day and time of THE MAGIC SCHOOL BUS show.
- Call your nearest PBS station for the scheduled sequence of episodes.

## TAPE THE SHOW!
- **THE MAGIC SCHOOL BUS** can be taped off the air for use in classrooms and community group settings, as long as the tapes are erased after three years.
- **THE MAGIC SCHOOL BUS** is closed-captioned for the hearing impaired.

# Using This Activity Guide

This guide is designed to help you use the television show as a supplement to your curriculum. Whether you use a few episodes or the entire series, the activities provided build on children's interest in THE MAGIC SCHOOL BUS and offer lots of opportunities to engage them in hands-on learning. Here's an overview of sections of the guide, which covers the first season.

## Activities

This section covers each episode on two pages. The first page is directed to you and contains four main parts outlined below. The second page is the children's activity sheet. You can make copies as needed.

- **Ms. Frizzle's Ideas for the Day:** brief statement of the main science idea.
- **Reports:** child's-eye view of the science content.
- **Field Trip Notes:** TV episode plot summary that describes the science discoveries along with the action and adventure.
- **Going Hands-On:** step-by-step directions that go with the children's activity page.

## Other Activities

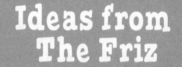

Write To Us!

Your kids can write to the show. Copy **Write the Producer** (page 3) for them to ask questions and explain what they know. Tell how you use THE MAGIC SCHOOL BUS project by writing to: Friz Fans, Attn: CM, 740 Broadway, 8th floor, New York, NY 10003.

Science is everywhere, and attitudes toward science can be shaped at home. **Catch THE MAGIC SCHOOL BUS** provides information about the show, tells how to tune in, and suggests ways to have fun with science. There's even a hands-on **Home Activity** with step-by-step instructions. Make copies of pages 4 and 5 for kids to take home.

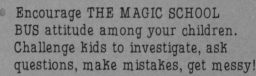

Get Families Involved

With copies of **Make Your Own Books** (page 32), children can use the drawings of the show's characters to help illustrate their own work.

## Ideas from The Friz

- Encourage THE MAGIC SCHOOL BUS attitude among your children. Challenge kids to investigate, ask questions, make mistakes, get messy!

- If you see your students following traditional gender roles, encourage both girls and boys to take part in everything.

- Give students lots of opportunities to manipulate, test, and question their science ideas using everyday materials.

- Set up a science center where children can work independently to explore topics they want to know more about. Provide books, posters, and, if possible, a computer, video tapes, and a video monitor.

- Take field trips. Visit your own backyard, a nearby sidewalk, or a local park. Or go to planetariums, museums, gardens, swamps, seashores, bakeries, restaurants, hospitals, or science labs.

- Share THE MAGIC SCHOOL BUS books during reading time.

- Encourage children to write their own stories or plays about amazing field trips.

- Help organize a science fair. Exhibit your MAGIC SCHOOL BUS projects.

- Take the bus concept and use it to explore geography, history, math, or any other subject.

# Write the Producer

At the end of each episode, children call THE MAGIC SCHOOL BUS Producer to ask questions or tell him something that wasn't included in the show. Here is your chance to tell the producer what you know. Send to: THE MAGIC SCHOOL BUS Producer, 740 Broadway, 8th Floor, New York, NY, 10003.

## Dear Magic School Bus Producer:

Wait a minute! You left some things out of the show about _____

_____

For example, _____

_____

_____

Not everything you showed is true! How could _____

_____

_____

And did you know that in real life this is true?

_____

_____

_____

One more thing I've always wanted to know is _____

_____

_____

signed _____

grade _____

school _____

address _____

# CATCH THE MAGIC SCHOOL BUS
## Television Series

## Dear Parent,

Welcome aboard THE MAGIC SCHOOL BUS! This new animated television series on PBS is based on Scholastic's award-winning book series by Joanna Cole and Bruce Degen. Each half-hour episode offers action-packed science adventures for six- to nine-year-olds, with educational and entertainment appeal for those younger and older.

Join Ms. Frizzle, the wonderfully weird teacher, and her enthusiastic students as they take amazing field trips on the Magic School Bus. The Bus can shrink and drive through an ant colony. It can blast off and take the class into outer space. Each episode is an adventure exploring a different science idea.

### Enjoy!

**CATCH THE MAGIC SCHOOL BUS WITH YOUR CHILD.**

It's another way to support your child's learning.

Check your local TV listings for the day and time.

**THE MAGIC SCHOOL BUS** is closed-captioned for the hearing impaired.

## MS. FRIZZLE'S TIPS FOR FAMILY SCIENCE FUN

- Take field trips together. Visit a park, library, planetarium, museum, or beach.
- Take field trips at home. Bake a cake in the kitchen, look at bugs in the backyard, or grow a house plant.
- Talk about science that you see every day. Ask questions and look for the answers together.

Get ready to try the Home Activity Check Out the Weather. It'll blow you away!

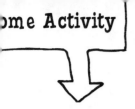

# Check Out the Weather

Watch the weather forecast on television or read it in the newspaper. Are the predictions correct? Make this wind streamer and find out which way the wind is coming from. How does knowing the direction of the wind help you predict the weather?

**What You Need**
- a paper bag
- crepe paper
- four 2-foot lengths of string
- tape
- scissors
- a compass

### What To Do

1. Cut out the bottom of the paper bag.

2. Cut the crepe paper into four pieces, each about two feet long and two inches wide. Tape each piece to the bottom of the bag.

3. Tape each piece of string to a corner at the other end of the bag. Tie the ends of the string together.

4. Take the wind streamer outside. Hang it or hold it up in a place where it can catch the wind.

Watch your wind streamer. See if you can tell which way the wind is coming from each day. Talk about it: Does the weather always come from the same direction? Record your observations.

It's your job to look for weather patterns!

**Sample**
wind direction:
**north**
weather report:
**rainy**

**Monday**
wind direction:
_____
weather report:
_____

**Tuesday**
wind direction:
_____
weather report:
_____

**Wednesday**
wind direction:
_____
weather report:
_____

**Thursday**
wind direction:
_____
weather report:
_____

**Friday**
wind direction:
_____
weather report:
_____

# The Magic School Bus
## Dries Up

### Field Trip Notes

Phoebe forms Students Against Desert Scarcity—SADS for short—to rescue desert animals from their harsh living conditions. Ms. Frizzle's class flies off to the desert in the Magic School Bus-turned-airplane. There the kids try to save different animals, but each one seems to manage without the children's help. The class, on the other hand, is hot, thirsty, and cranky when a thunderstorm suddenly sweeps in. Will the kids be washed away in a flash flood? Or will the rain give them a fresh look at the desert?

### How the Kangaroo Rat Lives in the Desert
#### by Phoebe

The kangaroo rat gets water from the seeds and plant parts it eats. It comes out at night, when the desert is cooler. To keep from being eaten by owls and other enemies, the kangaroo rat can change direction quickly as it hops.

## GOING HANDS-ON

### What You Need
(for each group)

- 4 bite-size pieces of different foods (Try apple, turkey, cheese, bread, chips.)
- 4 plastic sandwich bags that zip close
- gooseneck lamp with 75-watt bulb
- copies of WHERE'S THE WATER? page

### Where's the Water?
Adapted from *SuperScience Red*, Feb. 1992

For once, Arnold is prepared for a field trip! He's wearing desert survival gear. But the class discovers that desert animals have "built-in" adaptations, or ways of surviving. One adaptation many desert animals have is the ability to get water from their food. Have children work in small groups to find out if foods they eat contain water.

### Talk About It

Ask children if they think there is water in the food they eat. Why? Together, make a list of foods that kids think contain water.

### What To Do

1. Give each group the materials.
2. Arrange a spot for kids to place bags about 20 inches under the lamp.
3. Help kids discover if the foods contain water. Have them write their responses on the WHERE'S THE WATER? page. (The moisture from the food evaporates and condenses in the sandwich bag.)

### Next Stop

Ask children: What foods would you want to take with you if you were going on a hike in the desert?

name: _____

date: _____

# Where's the Water?

Write the name of the food in each bag on the labels.

Find out if different foods you eat contain water.
1. Put one piece of food in each plastic bag and seal.
2. Place the bags under the lamp.

#1        #2        #3        #4

## PREDICTIONS

Which food do you think will have the most water? _____

Why? _____

Which food do you think will have the least water? _____

Why? _____

## OBSERVATIONS   After waiting half an hour, look at the bags.

Which food has the most water in it? _____

How can you tell? _____

Which food has the least? _____

How can you tell? _____

Do all the food pieces have some water? _____

How can you tell? _____

# The Magic School Bus
## For Lunch

### Field Trip Notes

Arnold's dream comes true! Ms. Frizzle lets him skip the field trip. What he doesn't know is that HE is the field trip: The Bus takes the rest of the class on a rip-roaring ride through Arnold's digestive system. When they arrive at the large intestine, the kids refuse to finish the trip as waste products. Instead, they exit Arnold by traveling back up his digestive system. With the help of a burp, the class returns, and Arnold's friends give him a trophy for being the best field trip ever!

### What Happens to Food You Eat?
#### by Wanda

After you chew and swallow food, it goes through the esophagus to the stomach, then into the small intestine. From there the tiny food pieces go into the bloodstream and travel to all parts of the body. The waste products move through the large intestine and out the anus.

## GOING HANDS-ON

### Food Crushers
Adapted from *SuperScience Red*, Feb. 1993

When the Magic School Bus shrinks and goes into Arnold's mouth, the children watch his teeth chew Cheezie Wheezies while the Bus swerves to avoid being crushed! The kids meet up with much smaller pieces of the Cheezie Wheezies again in the stomach. It's all part of the normal digestive process. In this activity, children can explore the mouth, where digestion begins.

### What You Need

- small mirrors
- paper plates
- a piece of apple, banana, and celery for each child
- copies of FOOD CRUSHERS page

### Talk About It

Ask children: Where do you think digestion begins? What happens to food in the mouth?

### What To Do

1. Give children copies of the FOOD CRUSHERS page. Have them wash their hands before beginning the activity.
2. Have kids look at their teeth in the mirror
3. Pass around plates with the food.
4. Help children make and record their observations on the activity page.

### Next Stop

Ask children: How does chewing food help the body digest it? What happens to the pieces of food along the digestive tract?

# Food Crushers

## OBSERVE
Look at your front and back teeth in the mirror.

How are they alike?          How are they different?

_____          _____

_____          _____

**1. Bite the apple. Did you use your front teeth or back teeth to take the bite?**

_____

**2. Chew the bite of apple. (It's OK to swallow it, too.) Did you use your front or back teeth to chew?**

_____

**3. Eat a piece of banana and a piece of celery. Which teeth do the most work when you bite . . .**

the banana?

_____

the celery?

_____

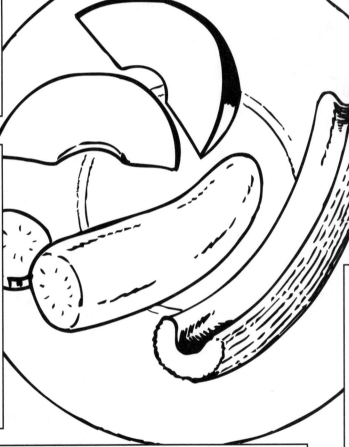

**4. What work does your tongue do when you eat the banana?**

_____

_____

_____

_____

_____

_____

## THINK ABOUT IT
Can you think of other foods you eat with your

front teeth? _____

back teeth? _____

tongue? _____

# The Magic School Bus
# Gets Ants in Its Pants

## Field Trip Notes

What project can Ms. Frizzle's class do for the Science Fair? How about a movie about an ant colony? Keesha is the director in search of a star for the show. When the class shrinks and travels through an ant hill, she finds ants doing different tasks. But no one ant seems right for the starring role. By the end of the field trip, the kids discover that ants communicate and work together to help one another live. All the ants are stars!

### Ants Depend on Each Other
#### by Keesha

Every ant has a job to do to keep the nest going. Forager ants find food and carry it back to the nest. The queen lays the eggs and nurse ants take care of the young. Guard ants protect the nest. Builder ants make and repair the nest.

## GOING HANDS-ON

## Be Observ-ANT

What's the best way to get to know ants better? The Magic School Bus kids try working with the ants. They watch the ants and figure out what they're doing. Your kids can observe ants doing some tasks by making them a temporary indoor home.

### What You Need

- one-quart (or larger) glass jar
- shovel
- ant hill
- piece of aluminum foil
- rubber bands or tape
- black construction paper
- cotton ball soaked with sugar water
- bits of fruit or honey-soaked bread
- copies of BE OBSERV-ANT page

### Talk About It

Ask children: What do you think the ants will need to do in their indoor home?

### What To Do

1. Scoop up part of an ant hill and put the soil and ants in the jar. Make sure these are not fire ants or other ants that can hurt you.

2. Cover the top of the jar with the foil and secure with a rubber band. Punch pin hol in the foil.

3. Put black construction paper around the jar to give the ants a dark environment. Secure the paper with tape or rubber ban

4. Put the cotton ball on the soil. Ask kids: What do you think the ants will do with this sugar water-soaked cotton?

5. Place food pieces on the soil. Ask kids: What do you think the ants will do with this food? Put the cover back on the jar.

6. Remove the black paper each day so small groups of kids can observe the ants.

7. Keep the ant home for a week, then return the ants to where you got them.

### Next Stop

Observe ants outside. Kids can place pieces of honey-soaked bread nearby and see how the ants react.

Scholastic's
The Magic
School Bus™

# Be
# Observ-ANT

**OBSERVE**
Write about things you see the ants doing.

## Day 1
_____
_____
_____

## Day 2
_____
_____
_____

## Day 3
_____
_____
_____

## Day 4
_____
_____
_____

## Day 5
_____

How are the ants helping one another?
_____
_____
_____

On the back, draw a picture of one thing you saw the ants doing.

# The Magic School Bus
## Gets Baked in a Cake

### Field Trip Notes

Whoops! It's Ms. Frizzle's birthday, and the kids are planning a surprise—but they've forgotten the cake. A field trip to a bakery seems like the perfect solution. The kids accidentally get shrunk to ingredient size, but still manage to make cake batter and learn about chemistry in the process. Then the baker pours them into the cake pan along with the batter. The Bus is getting baked! Can what they've learned about chemistry save the Magic School Bus kids?

### Cooking Is Chemistry
#### by Carlos

In chemistry, parts are mixed together to make something new. In the kitchen, the parts are called ingredients. When we cook, we mix ingredients together to make a completely new thing. Flour, sugar, salt, eggs, milk, and other ingredients are mixed together to make a cake.

## GOING HANDS-ON

### Pretzel Chemistry

Is it baking—or chemistry? Ms. Frizzle's class learns that baking is like doing a chemistry experiment. Your kids can make chemistry happen as they follow this recipe for pretzels. You or another adult can help groups of four to eight kids bake batches of pretzels. If you do not have access to an oven, make the dough with children and let them carry portions home in plastic bags to make with their families.

### What You Need

- copies of PRETZEL CHEMISTRY page
- utensils and ingredients from the recipe
- an oven

### What To Do

As you follow the recipe, encourage children to talk about the changes they observe, and ask:

1. What happens when you add yeast and honey to the warm water? (The mixture makes bubbles and smells yeasty. The yeast cells feed on sugar and release carbon dioxide.)

2. What happens after you knead the dough and let it sit? (The carbon dioxide makes the dough rise.)

3. What happens to the pretzel shapes while they're baking? (They get fatter.)

### Next Stop

Kids can put vinegar and baking soda in a soda bottle, and place a balloon over the top of the bottle. What happens?

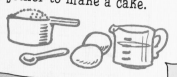

# Pretzel Chemistry

# MEGAPRETZELS

This recipe will make
8-10 large pretzels.

## WHAT YOU NEED

### UTENSILS
- mixing bowl
- greased bowl
- cutting board
- clean dish towel
- wooden spoon
- greased cookie sheet

### INGREDIENTS
- 1/4 ounce package or 1/2 tablespoon active dry yeast
- 1/2 cup warm water
- 1 tablespoon honey
- 1 teaspoon salt
- 1 1/2 cups flour
- 1/4 cup flour (to sprinkle on cutting board)
- 3 tablespoons melted butter
- extra salt

## WHAT TO DO

1. Stir yeast into the warm water. Add honey and salt. Let sit about 5 minutes.

2. Stir in 1 1/2 cups flour to make a thick mixture.

3. Sprinkle 1/4 cup flour (as needed) on a cutting board. Knead dough on the board for 5-7 minutes.

4. Put dough in greased bowl and cover with the dish towel. Let dough sit at room temperature about 20 minutes.

5. Roll out long thin pieces of dough and make shapes or letters. Place these on a greased cookie sheet.

**An Adult Needs to Help with These Steps**

6. Pre-heat oven to 475° for 5 minutes.

7. Pour melted butter over pretzels. Sprinkle salt.

8. Bake pretzels for 10-12 minutes.

9. Enjoy!

> What happens to the mixture?

> Why is there wait time here? What happens to the dough?

> What happens to the shapes as they cook?

> Take chances! Make mistakes! And especially . . . Get messy!

# The Magic School Bus
# Gets Eaten

### Field Trip Notes

Arnold and Keesha forget their homework—to bring in two beach things that go together—so they improvise. He has a shoe filled with pond scum he stepped in on the way to school. She has a tuna sandwich for her lunch. Ms. Frizzle thinks it's a brilliant combination. On the class field trip to the ocean, Arnold and Keesha search for the connection between scum and tuna. The Bus and class shrink, travel through the food chain—and get eaten by a tuna fish! From inside the tuna's stomach, Keesha makes the connection. Scum is a kind of algae and algae and tuna are part of the same food chain. Now, if they can just get out of that fish!

### An Ocean Food Chain
#### by Keesha

Phytoplankton are very tiny plants that live near the ocean surface. Like other plants, phytoplankton use the sun's energy to make their own food. Tiny animals called zooplankton eat phytoplankton. Anchovies eat zooplankton. And tuna eat anchovies. These are all links in an ocean food chain.

## GOING HANDS-ON

## Popcorn Chain

The Magic School Bus kids really get into the food chain: They're swallowed by a tuna fish. With this activity, your kids get to eat while they act as links in the food chain. The popcorn bags stand for food energy that is passed along the links in a food chain from the sun, to plants, to plant-eaters, to meat-eaters.

### Talk About It

Ask children: What is a food chain? What are some examples of plants and animals that are links in a food chain? What might happen in a food chain if one link is harmed by pollution?

### What You Need
- copies of **POPCORN CHAIN** page
- scissors
- markers
- yarn
- tape
- 12 baggies of popcorn

### What To Do

1. Choose roles for children: 1 sun, 12 plants, 6 plant-eaters, and 3 meat-eaters.

2. Kids color and cut out their symbols and tape them to yarn to make necklaces.

3. Have children spread out around the room or go outside if possible.

4. The sun holds all 12 bags of popcorn. She gives one bag to each plant.

5. The plants eat half of the popcorn to have energy for growing and living.

6. Each plant-eater takes a bag from two plants and eats half of the remaining popcorn.

7. Each meat-eater takes a bag from two plant-eaters and eats the rest of the popcorn.

### Next Stop

Kids can trace a food chain from a favorite food. They might try pizza, a jelly bean, or tuna fish.

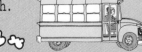

Scholastic's
The Magic
School Bus ™

# Popcorn Chain

**One example is:**

**Draw a picture of a food chain.**
Show where the food energy comes from. Show what eats what.

It's your job as scientists to look for connections!

**GET READY FOR THE POPCORN CHAIN**
Color and cut out the symbol that matches your role in the food chain.

Tape it to a piece of yarn and wear it around your neck.

# The Magic School Bus Goes to Seed

## Field Trip Notes

The photographer from *Plant It!* Magazine is coming to photograph Ms. Frizzle's class garden. But Phoebe doesn't have a plant. She wants to get her plant from the garden at her old school and replant it in her new school garden. There isn't much time, so Ms. Frizzle turns the Magic School Bus into a tiny ladybug-bus and flies the class to the other school's garden. The kids get a bug's-eye view of the flower world and find out how seeds are created, how they travel, and how they grow into plants. Will the class be able to get the seed from Phoebe's plant back to their garden? Can Ms. Frizzle sprout the seed in time for the photo shoot?

### What Is a Seed?
#### by Phoebe

A seed is a plant waiting to happen. Inside every seed is a tiny baby plant with a tiny root, stem, and one or two tiny leaves.

## GOING HANDS-ON

## Seeds on the Move

Adapted from *SuperScience Red*, Oct. 1993

Ms. Frizzle's class hangs on inside the tiny Magic School Bus as it hitches a ride on a wind-traveling seed. The seed travels by clinging to an animal—in this case, a man on a bicycle!

### What You Need

- different seeds (such as maple tree, sunflower, cockleburs)
- cups of water
- stuffed animals
- copies of SEEDS ON THE MOVE page

### Talk About It
Ask children: Have you ever seen seeds travel? How did they move?

### What To Do
1. Each child chooses three seeds to test.
2. On the chart, children write the name of each seed and draw a picture of it.
3. Have kids guess how they think each seed travels, then circle wind, water, or hitchhiker under PREDICTION on the chart.
4. Kids test each seed and circle results under OBSERVATION on the chart.

**Wind Test:** Hold the seed in the air and let it drop. If it drifts, it shows how a seed can travel by wind.

**Water Test:** Drop seeds into a cup of water and stir. The ones that float show how seeds can travel by water.

**Hitchhiker Test:** Put a stuffed animal on top of each seed, press down, then lift up the animal. The seeds that stick show how seeds can travel by sticking to an animal.

### Finding Seeds
Do this activity in the autumn. You can find wind-traveling seeds from late fall flowers. Pick up hitchhikers by walking among weeds in a vacant lot or field. Buy sunflower or other seeds that can float to demonstrate how seeds can travel by water.

### Next Stop
Give kids materials to make their own wind traveler, water traveler, or hitchhiker seeds. Have a friend test the seeds to find out how they travel.

# Seeds on the Move

How do you think each seed could travel? By wind, water, or as a hitchhiker?
Make a guess and test it.  Then record what happens.

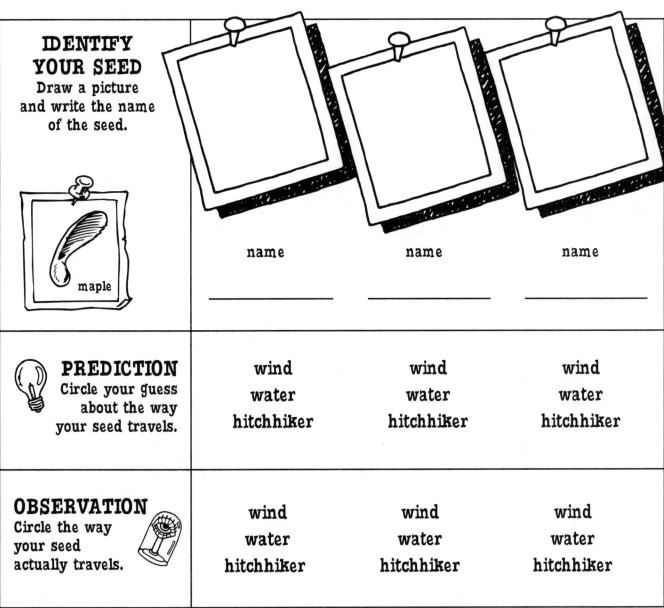

| IDENTIFY YOUR SEED<br>Draw a picture and write the name of the seed. | name<br>_____ | name<br>_____ | name<br>_____ |
|---|---|---|---|
| maple | | | |
| PREDICTION<br>Circle your guess about the way your seed travels. | wind<br>water<br>hitchhiker | wind<br>water<br>hitchhiker | wind<br>water<br>hitchhiker |
| OBSERVATION<br>Circle the way your seed actually travels. | wind<br>water<br>hitchhiker | wind<br>water<br>hitchhiker | wind<br>water<br>hitchhiker |

Draw a picture on the back of this sheet showing the way one of your seeds travels.

# The Magic School Bus
# Hops Home

### Ms. Frizzle's Ideas for the Day

- A habitat is a plant or animal's home. Different kinds of plants and animals often share a habitat.
- A habitat meets an animal's needs: food, shelter, a place to raise young, safety from predators.

### Field Trip Notes

Wanda brings Bella, her pet bullfrog, to school and starts to set up a habitat for her in the classroom. Bella has other ideas, however. She hops out the window and heads for parts unknown. The class hops after her—in the Magic School Bus turned bullfrog. After searching in a few habitats, the kids find Bella in a lovely pond that's just right for a frog to live in. But how will Bella escape the predator heron? And if Bella lives there, won't Wanda be lonely without her?

### A Pond Is a Bullfrog's Habitat
#### by Wanda

A pond habitat has everything a bullfrog needs. There are insects to eat and calm water to swim and lay eggs in. A bullfrog has space to hop around and places to hide from predators.

## GOING HANDS-ON

## Earth-Wormery

What does an animal need in its habitat? Wanda learns that her pet bullfrog needs food, water, shelter, and a place to raise its young.

*Closed environment*

Your kids can work in groups to set up temporary indoor homes for earthworms. They can observe the earthworms in an environment that is similar to the natural one.

*Open for viewing*

### What You Need
(for each group)

- one-quart jar
- moist soil from where earthworms live
- 4 or 5 earthworms
- pieces of grass or dead leaves
- black construction paper
- tape or rubber band
- food: dry oatmeal, cornmeal
- water
- copies of EARTH-WORMERY page

### Talk About It

Ask children: Where does an earthworm live? What does it need to live?

### What To Do

1. Dig up moist soil and earthworms.
2. Give children materials to make the habitats and help them set up according to the directions on the EARTH-WORMERY page.
3. Children can record their observations.

### Next Stop

Help children choose a small area outdoors where they can observe animals. Have them look quietly for five minutes. They can bring notebooks and record what they see.

name: _____

date: _____

# Earth-Wormery

Set up the earthworms' indoor home.

## WHAT TO DO

1. Fill the jar about three-quarters full with the soil.
2. Mix the dry food and grass or dead leaves into the soil.
3. Put 4-5 earthworms in the jar.
4. Sprinkle water each day to make the soil damp, but not wet.
5. Cover the jar with the black paper. Keep it closed with rubber band or tape.
6. After observing the earthworms, return them to their natural habitat.

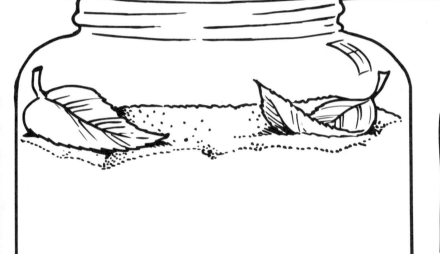

## OBSERVATIONS

Write about what you see the earthworms doing each day.

### Day 1
_____
_____
_____

### Day 2
_____
_____
_____

### Day 3
_____
_____
_____

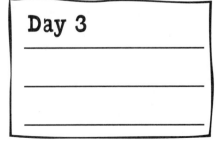

Draw a picture of your earthworm observations.

# The Magic School Bus in the Haunted House

### Ms. Frizzle's Idea for the Day

- Sound begins when something moves, or vibrates. When the vibration stops, the sound stops.

### Field Trip Notes

It all starts when Ms. Frizzle's class is rehearsing *Concerto for Invented Instrument.* Carlos's invented instrument looks great, but sounds "ploopy." Ms. Frizzle takes the kids to the Sound Museum—which is a spooky old house on a lonely hill, full of mysterious sounds. The children explore the Soundscape Room, hearing sounds from jungle, mountain, sea, and city environments. In another room, the kids feel vibrations when they play giant musical instruments. They put on special glasses and see sound waves in the Sound-O-Vision room. Can Carlos learn how to get the right sound from his musical instrument in time for the concert?

### How Does Sound Travel?
#### by Carlos

Sound vibrations travel as waves. They can travel through air, water, wood, glass, or other material. A sound vibration spreads out in all directions from its source, like ripples in a pond.

SPLASH!

## GOING HANDS-ON

### What You Need
(for each group)

- clean empty soup can
- a can opener
- plastic wrap or a balloon with open end cut off
- rubber band
- a few grains of rice
- a radio or tape cassette player
- copies of SEE SOUND page
- objects for making musical instruments: rubber bands, wooden or cardboard boxes, cans, jars, pebbles, beans, paper clips

### See Sound

When the Magic School Bus kids play giant musical instruments, they see and feel the vibrations. Your kids can see—as well as hear—the results of vibrations in this activity. Have children work in small groups.

### Talk About It

Have children put their hands on their throats, then speak, sing, or hum. Can they feel the vibrations?

### What To Do

1. Remove the top and bottom lids of the cans. Don't leave any sharp edges.

2. Cover one end of each can with plastic wrap. Secure it in place with the rubber band.

3. Give each group a can, the rice, and a radio or tape player. Give each child a copy of the SEE SOUND page.

4. After children try the experiment and write their responses in the chart, they can make their own instruments. Give them the objects to put together any way they want.

### Next Stop

Children can work in groups to make up their own *Concerto for Invented Instruments.*

name: _____

date: _____

Scholastic's
The Magic
School Bus ™

# See Sound

What happens to the rice when sound comes out of the speaker?

**1.** Put the can on top of the speaker.

**2.** Put the rice grains on top of the plastic.

**3.** Think about it. What will happen when the radio is turned on loud? Soft?

**4.** Record your observations.

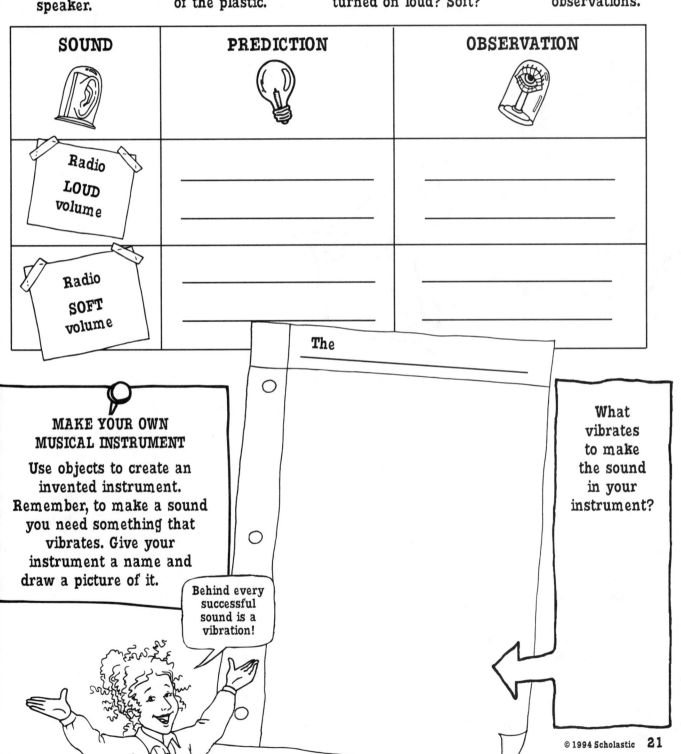

| SOUND | PREDICTION | OBSERVATION |
|---|---|---|
| Radio LOUD volume | | |
| Radio SOFT volume | | |

The _____

**MAKE YOUR OWN MUSICAL INSTRUMENT**

Use objects to create an invented instrument. Remember, to make a sound you need something that vibrates. Give your instrument a name and draw a picture of it.

Behind every successful sound is a vibration!

What vibrates to make the sound in your instrument?

# The Magic School Bus
## Inside Ralphie

### Field Trip Notes

There's action! Adventure! Excitement! All inside Ralphie's body. He's sick and has to stay home from school. So Ms. Frizzle and the class take the Magic School Bus to Ralphie's bedroom. They shrink, go inside his body, and travel in his bloodstream to his sore throat. The kids find out what's making Ralphie sick, and see his white blood cells fight the bacteria in a raging battle. Ralphie's winning! But there's one problem. Now the white blood cells think the Magic School Bus is a germ. How can the class escape?

### How Does Your Body Fight Germs When You're Sick?
#### by Ralphie

There are red blood cells and white blood cells in your blood. The white blood cells search out germs and get rid of them. Some white blood cells "eat" germs. Others make antibodies to fight germs and keep them from spreading.

red blood cells

white blood cell

## GOING HANDS-ON

## Skin to Germs: KEEP OUT!

The Magic School Bus gets inside Ralphie's body by going through a cut on his leg. Germs *can* get into the body that way, too. But usually the skin protects the body. Set up this activity to show how skin protects our bodies the way apple skin protects an apple.

### Talk About It

As you set up the activity, ask: What do you think will happen to each apple in one week?

### What You Need

- 2 sheets of paper
- 2 apples with no cuts or blemishes
- table knife
- copies of SKIN TO GERMS: KEEP OUT! page

### What To Do

1. Label the sheets of paper A and B.
2. Wash hands and the apples. Place one apple on each sheet.
3. With the knife, peel back the skin to leave four openings about 1/2 inch in diameter on apple B.
4. Get an assistant with unwashed hands to rub her hands all around the apples.
5. Watch the apples for a week. Do not touch them. Each day, kids can write down their observations.

### Next Stop

Ask kids: What is the purpose of the skin on an apple? How does the skin of an apple work like the skin of your body?

# Skin to Germs: KEEP OUT!

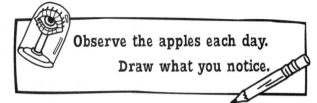

Observe the apples each day.
Draw what you notice.

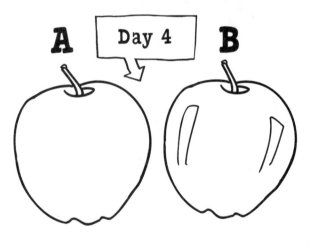

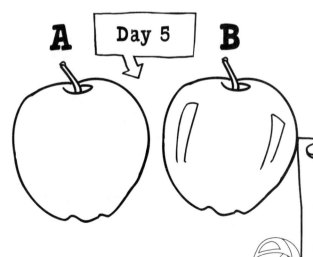

What changes did you see in the apples?

_____

_____

Skin is tough!

# The Magic School Bus Kicks Up a Storm

## Field Trip Notes

Can anyone do something about the weather? It's a hot, muggy day and a thunderstorm might help break the heat. Ralphie fantasizes being a superhero—Weatherman—who controls the weather. He gets to live out his daydream when the class rides the Magic School Bus into the clouds. As Weatherman, Ralphie makes wind, an updraft, clouds, and rain. Then a thunderstorm moves in and the Magic School Bus is caught in the middle of it! Can Weatherman save the day?

### What Is Wind?
#### by Keesha

Wind is air moving from one spot on Earth to another. When the Sun shines on the Earth, the air near the ground heats up. Warm air is lighter than cool air, so it rises. Cooler air moves in to take its place. This moving air is wind!

## GOING HANDS-ON

## Wind Spiral

Weatherman (a/k/a/ Ralphie) mixes heat with air to create an updraft, and the Magic School Bus rides high into the sky! Your kids can see a small updraft by making wind spirals.

### What To Do

1. Have kids decorate and cut out their spirals.

2. Help them pull the needle and thread through the X on the spiral.

3. Demonstrate how the spirals can turn in moving air. Hold one spiral up high by the string. Blow gently from underneath.

4. Turn the lamp facing up. Let each child hold her spiral over the light bulb.

### Talk About It

Ask children: Why does the warm air from the lamp affect the spiral the same way blowing from underneath it does?

### Next Stop

Next time it rains, your kids can make a rain gauge. Place a clear glass jar outside in an open space. Use a ruler to measure how much rain fell.

### What You Need
(for each child)

- a copy of WIND SPIRAL page
- crayons or markers
- scissors
- needle
- thread in 1-foot-long pieces
- gooseneck lamp with 75-watt light bulb

name: _____

date: _____

1. Decorate your spiral.
   Cut it out along the dotted line.

2. Pull needle
   and thread
   through the
   X on the
   spiral. Tie a
   knot at the
   end of the
   thread so it
   will hold up
   the spiral.

3. To see how
   warm air
   rises, hold
   your spiral
   over the
   light bulb.

X

What happens?

_____

_____

# The Magic School Bus
## Lost in Space

### Field Trip Notes

This time Arnold *wants* to go on a field trip—so his show-off cousin Janet can see what a great teacher Ms. Frizzle is. The Bus becomes a spaceship and the class visits the Sun, Mercury, Venus, and Mars. When an asteroid hits the "spaceship," Ms. Frizzle puts on a jet pack and goes outside to make repairs. By accident, The Friz jets away into space, leaving the kids alone on the Bus. The class is lost in space without a teacher! Can the kids use what they know to find Ms. Frizzle and get back home?

### The Planets in the Solar System
#### by Ralphie

All nine planets travel around the Sun in paths called orbits. The planets are different sizes and are different distances from the Sun. Some are very hot and others are cold. Some are rocky and some are mostly gas.

**GOING HANDS-ON**

## Discover the Planets

When Ms. Frizzle jets away into space, she talks with the kids by radio. She gives hints for her students to find her—and to identify the planets as they go. In this activity, your kids identify the planets by making two models of the Solar System. The first shows the order of the planets and the second shows the planets' relative sizes.

### What You Need

- copies of DISCOVER THE PLANETS page
- stick-on labels
- markers
- items to represent planets: basketball (Jupiter), soccer ball (Saturn), 2 softballs (Uranus, Neptune), 2 Ping Pong balls (Earth, Venus), 1 jacks ball (Mars), 2 marbles (Mercury, Pluto)
- books on the Solar System

### Talk About It

Ask: What are the names of the planets in the Solar System? What order are they in?

### What To Do

1. Give children copies of the DISCOVER THE PLANETS page.

2. Have kids do "Be a Planet" in groups of 10. Children can be the Sun or one of the nine planets. Each child makes a label showing the planet (or the Sun) that he or she stands for.

3. Give groups the balls and marbles to do "Make a Model." Children can show the approximate size of the planets in relation to one another by lining up the round objects in the order of the planets. Kilometers show the planets' diameters.

### Next Stop

Kids can write about a planet they like, telling its name, its location from the Sun, and what is special about it.

name: _____

date: _____

# Discover the Planets

## Be a Planet

Show the order of the planets in the Solar System.

1. Write the name and draw a picture of the planet or the Sun on your label.
2. Form a line showing the order of the planets from the Sun.
3. Then orbit around the Sun.

**Approximate diameters in kilometers**

Mercury 4,900 km

Venus 12,100 km

Earth 12,800 km

Mars 6,800 km

Jupiter 143,000 km

Saturn 121,000 km

Uranus 51,100 km

Neptune 49,500 km

Pluto 2,300 km

As I always say, class...you're out of this world!

## Make a Model

1. Look at the balls and marbles. These objects stand for the planets.
2. Place them in the order of the planets to make a model of the Solar System.

**27**

# The Magic School Bus Meets the Rot Squad

### Ms. Frizzle's Ideas for the Day

- Decomposition, or rot, is part of every life cycle.
- Plants and animals called decomposers naturally recycle once-living things. Many – such as fungi and bacteria – are too tiny to be seen.

## Field Trip Notes

Wanda wins the Most Disgusting Rot contest with her entry from the back of her refrigerator. First prize is a baby tree, and Wanda wants to plant it in a vacant lot nearby. The class takes the Magic School Bus to the lot, but the kids don't understand what a tree has to do with rot. To help them find out, Ms. Frizzle shrinks the Bus and the class travels through a rotting log in the lot. The kids discover that the "dead" log is teeming with life—it is both home and food for many plants and animals. And the rot is making rich soil—a perfect place for a new tree to grow!

### A Rotting Log Supports Life
#### by Wanda

Plants and animals live in a log. They also break the log down into smaller pieces that become part of the soil. New plants grow in this soil. So a rotting log is a plant and animal habitat *and* an example of nature's recycling!

## GOING HANDS-ON

## The Leaf-Decay Contraption

Adapted from *SuperScience Red*, Sept. 1992

Ms. Frizzle's class finds out how rot makes rich soil for new growth. Your kids can discover the connection between rot and leaves mixed in damp soil. Children can continue this experiment for a month or longer.

### Talk About It

Ask children: What rotting things have you seen? Where did you see them? Did you find fungi or insects in the decaying material?

### What You Need

- two 2-liter plastic soda bottles cut and labeled as shown
- 3"x 3" piece of pantyhose
- rubber band
- 1 cup garden soil
- 2-3 handfuls of dead leaves
- 1 cup rain water (or tap water left out overnight)
- crayon
- large spoon
- copies of THE LEAF-DECAY CONTRAPTION page

### What To Do

1. Help children set up and maintain the Leaf-Decay Contraption.

2. Ask kids: What do you think will happen to the leaf and soil mixture? Make a large chart to record the kids' weekly predictions and observations.

3. After completing the activity, discuss with children: Why do you think the le and soil mixture changed the way it d

### Next Stop

Besides leaves, what other things rot? Children can start a compost heap with discarded vegetable scraps from lunches c snacks, and watch the decomposition.

# The Leaf-Decay Contraption

## What To Do

**1.** Cut and label the soda bottles like this:

**2.** Put the stocking piece over the spout of B. Secure it with a rubber band.

**3.** Set B, small end down, inside A.

**4.** Mix the leaves with the soil. Put the mixture inside B and gently pack it down. With the crayon, mark on B where the top of the mixture reaches.

**5.** Loosen the cap on C. Set C, spout down, inside B.

**6.** Pour the rain water into C. The water will drip through the loosened cap, the leaves and soil, and down into A.

**7.** Keep the Leaf-Decay Contraption in a warm place, but not in the Sun. Each day, pour the water from A into C.

**8.** At the end of a week, stir the mixture and pack it down. Mark the top of the mixture again. Do this for a month or longer, if possible.

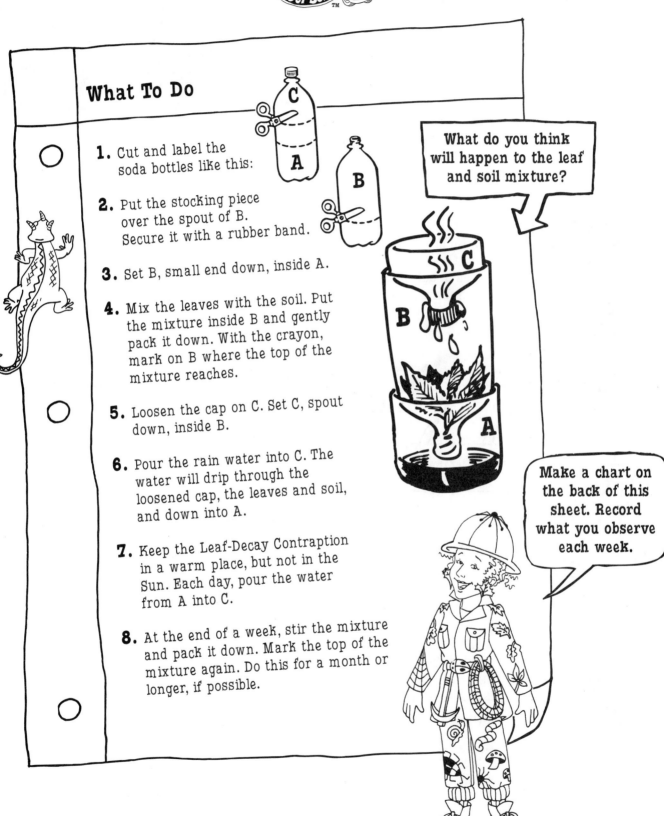

What do you think will happen to the leaf and soil mixture?

Make a chart on the back of this sheet. Record what you observe each week.

# The Magic School Bus
## Plays Ball

### Field Trip Notes

Ralphie's delighted! Ms. Frizzle's class is going to a baseball game. Of course, it's a very special baseball game. The Magic School Bus shrinks and takes Ms. Frizzle and the kids inside a book to a frictionless baseball field. Ralphie hits a homer he'd never have imagined in the world of friction, and all the kids find out about friction and other pushes and pulls. But when they get on the Bus to head back to school, the book closes with them inside it. How can they get out of the book? Can what they've learned about forces and friction help them make it home?

### What Makes a Ball Move?
#### by Ralphie

To start moving, a ball needs a force—a push or a pull.

A force can also change the direction or speed of the ball.

## GOING HANDS-ON

### What You Need
#### (for each group)

- shoe box
- popsicle stick
- large rubber band
- tape
- a copy of FRICTION ACTION page
- ruler
- table
- small stones to fit inside box
- rounded pencils or straws

## Friction Action

What a difference friction makes! When Ms. Frizzle's kids get off the Bus into the world of nonfriction, they can't even walk. Your kids can work in small groups to find how movement changes when there is more—and less—friction.

### Talk About It

Help children think about friction by asking: Where would be a good place to slide? Why?

### What To Do

1. Prepare a box for each group. Cut a small hole in one end. Pull the rubber band through the hole, loop it around the stick, and tape the stick in place.

2. Give each group a copy of the FRICTION ACTION page.

3. Help children follow the directions for the activity.

### Next Stop

Discuss other ways besides rollers to make less friction between the box and the table. Try putting marbles, sugar, or ice under the box.

name: _____

date: _____

# Friction Action

### Find out what happens when you pull the box.

| | | |
|---|---|---|
| **Fill box with stones. Put box on table.** | **PREDICTIONS**<br><br>Think about what will happen when you pull the box by the rubber band. Write how long you think the rubber band will stretch before the box moves.<br><br>inches | **OBSERVATIONS**<br><br>Pull the box. Measure how long the rubber band stretches before the box begins to move. Write the distance here.<br><br>inches |
| **Place rollers under box. Then record your predictions and observations.** | inches | inches |

Use this handy ruler to measure the distance.

0 in. ____
____
1 in. ____
____
2 in. ____
____
3 in. ____
____
4 in. ____
____
5 in. ____
____
6 in. ____
____
7 in. ____
____
8 in. ____
____
9 in. ____

# Make Your Own Books

Use these illustrations to create your own MAGIC SCHOOL BUS books, posters, advertisements, comics, or bulletin board displays.

RALPHIE

WANDA

MS. FRIZZLE

KEESHA

CARLOS

DOROTHY ANN

ARNOLD

PHOEBE

LIZ

TIM